Contents

Welcome to

The Natural History Museum

Welcome to The Natural History Museum, home of the nation's natural history collections. We have created this guide to help you discover what there is to see and do, so that you can plan your route around the Museum. We hope that you enjoy your visit.

Collections of over 68 million natural history specimens lie at the heart of the museum's work. This vast resource forms an unique database of life providing materials for a wide range of dynamic and stimulating exhibitions and unparalleled research opportunities. With a widely acknowledged reputation as a centre of excellence, the Museum plays a significant role in the international scientific community. Behind the scenes over 300 scientists and librarians collaborate with other research institutions and governments world – wide to extend our knowledge and understanding of the natural world.

How to plan your visit

The Museum is divided into the Life Galleries and the Earth Galleries. If you entered the Museum using the Cromwell Road entrance, you began your visit in the Life Galleries. If you used the Exhibition Road entrance, you began in the Earth Galleries. To find your way around using the Guide, note the gallery numbers of exhibitions you wish to see and refer to the map at the front of the Guide for their location. Signs throughout the Museum will help guide you through the galleries and information desk staff and their colleagues on duty in the public areas will be pleased to offer further help and information.

An avenue of bronze statues highlights key issues in our understanding of the Earth in Visions of Earth *Gallery 60*

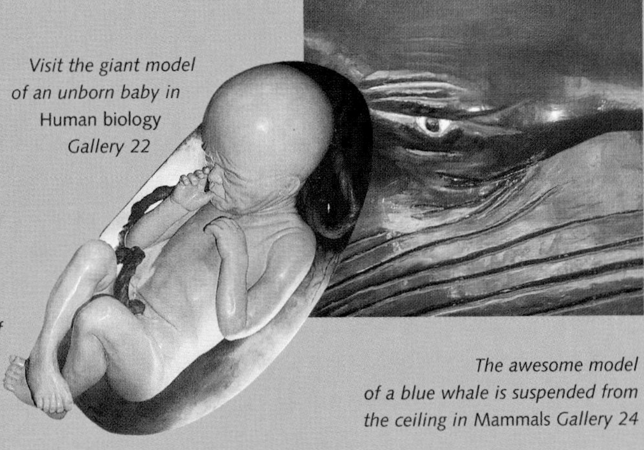

Visit the giant model of an unborn baby in Human biology *Gallery 22*

The awesome model of a blue whale is suspended from the ceiling in Mammals *Gallery 24*

Limited time?

If the amount of time you have to spend at the Museum is limited, we suggest you choose from our most popular exhibitions, listed below, or, if visiting with children, in the next colunm.

There are also opportunities join highlights and themed tours. Please ask at the Life Galleries information desk for further details.

- Wonders Gallery 10
- Dinosaurs Gallery 21
- Ecology Gallery 32
- The blue whale in Mammals Gallery 24
- The earthquake experience in The power within Gallery 61
- Earth's treasury Gallery 64

Your views on your visit are extremely important to us. It would be greatly appreciated if you could spare a few moments to complete the questionnaire attached to the free map you were given on admission. We hope you will return soon to revisit 'old favourites' and to explore and enjoy new exhibitions.

Children's choice

The exhibitions listed below are particular favourites amongst our younger visitors. To locate cloakrooms and baby changing and feeding rooms please consult the map at the front of the Guide or ask any uniformed member of staff for directions. The choice and location of refreshment facilities available is listed on page 50 of the Guide.

- Dinosaurs Gallery 21
- Mammals Galleries 23 and 24
- Creepy-crawlies Gallery 33
- Human biology Gallery 22
- Investigate – Room B2 (Basement, Life Galleries)
- The earthquake experience in The power within Gallery 61

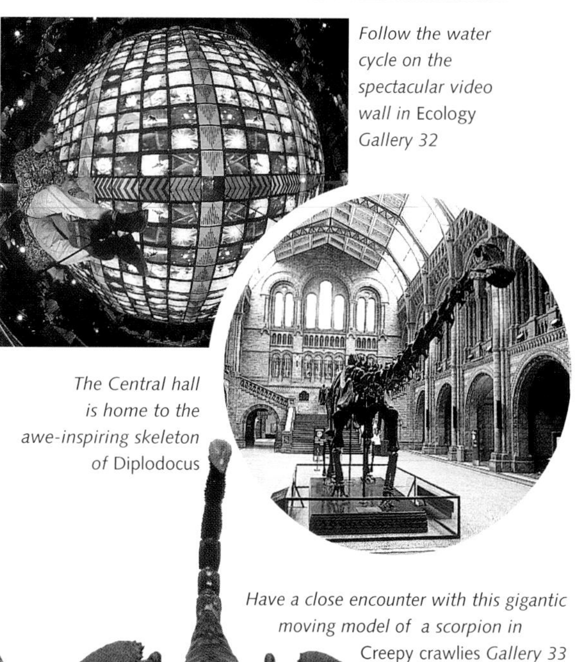

Follow the water cycle on the spectacular video wall in Ecology *Gallery 32*

The Central hall is home to the awe-inspiring skeleton of Diplodocus

Have a close encounter with this gigantic moving model of a scorpion in Creepy crawlies *Gallery 33*

The World's most advanced animatronic Tyrannosaurus rex *is waiting to meet you in* Dinosaurs *Gallery 21.*

Touch and handle remarkable natural objects in Investigate

Experience an earthquake as you stand in the reconstruction of a Japanese supermarket in The power within *Gallery 60*

10

Life
Galleries

(20minutes)
Ground floor
& first floor

Find yourself face to face with the dramatic and awe-inspiring skeleton of* Diplodocus *as you enter the Life Galleries. As you walk the entire 26-metre length of Britain's best loved dinosaur, you will encounter other exciting specimens from the Museum's unparalleled collections.

One of Alfred Waterhouse's beautifully decorated terracotta panels

Wonders of *The Natural History Museum*

The magnificent Central hall is itself an exhibit to stop and admire. Pause at the grand staircase and look up at the intricately painted ceiling. Pick out some of the hundreds of moulded terracotta monkeys, birds, flowers and reptiles, which run up columns and hide in the corners of arches. Climb the arched bridge staircase that leads to the second floor, and take in the spectacular view. This hall is home to some of the Museum's finest specimens, as well as computers which, through touch – screen technology, offer you guidance and information, in a variety of languages, on what the Museum has to offer.

A taster

Before you leave the Central hall look around the arched bays. Seek out a tiny nugget of gold and a giant lump of copper. Wonder at a tree trunk that has literally turned to stone, and a spider trapped in amber. Meet the coelacanth, which, until 1938, was thought to have been extinct for 70 million years. The Museum is yours to explore and enjoy.

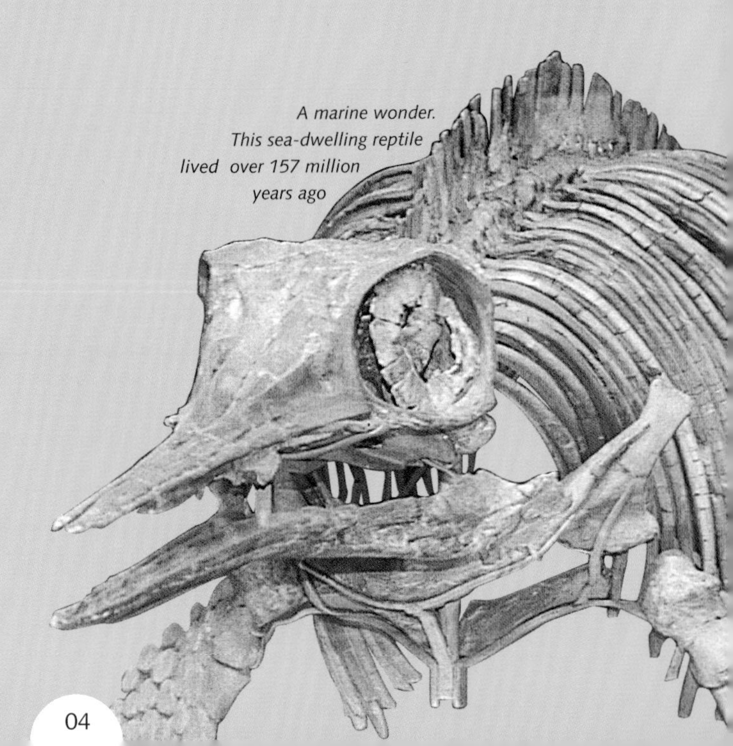

A marine wonder. This sea-dwelling reptile lived over 157 million years ago

The Central hall is home to the awe-inspiring skeleton of Diplodocus

Be dwarfed by a section of a giant sequoia tree on the second floor

Tall story

The giant sequoia tree, from which the section on the second floor was cut, was over 1,300 years old when it was felled. Follow the course of history by counting the annual rings. Giant sequoias grow up to 27 metres in circumference, and 80 metres high; 20 metres taller than the highest point of the Museum!

Waterhouse Way

Alfred Waterhouse was the architect of the Museum, which opened in 1881. His vision was of a cathedral-like building combining historical style with the latest methods of construction. He designed an iron and steel framework and covered it with beautifully decorated buff and pale-blue terracotta. Waterhouse Way is the 'spine' of his building, linking all the Life Galleries together; as you walk along it, you may notice that the terracotta decorations change. In the western wing they depict living species, while in the eastern, they illustrate extinct plants and animals.

A cast of the earliest known Pliosaur, *one of the highlights of* Waterhouse Way

12

Fishes amphibians

and reptiles

Life
Galleries

(30 minutes)
Ground floor

Enjoy an exhibition full of surprises; fish that live so deep they provide their own light, egg-eating snakes, pythons with hundreds of pairs of ribs and a 150-year-old giant tortoise.

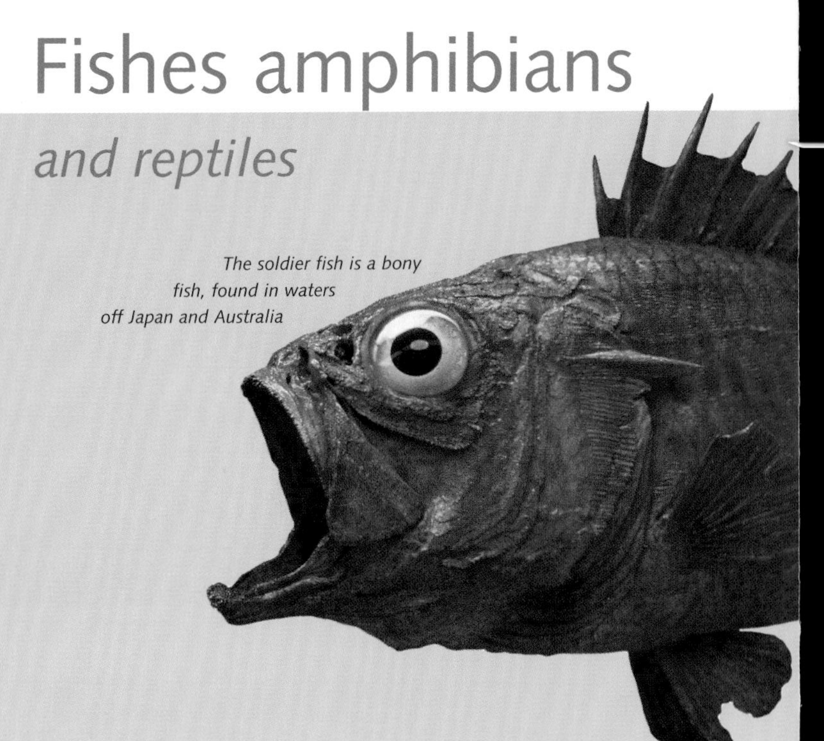

The soldier fish is a bony fish, found in waters off Japan and Australia

There are 20,000 species of fish; more than all other vertebrates put together. As well as the more familiar fish you may find, these wall displays contain some that live in the 'twilight zone' 400 metres down in the ocean, where there is little light; and others from the total darkness of the 'dark depths' at 1,000 metres. Most amphibians, a group that includes frogs, toads and newts, live part of their lives on land and return to the water to breed. Reptiles, such as lizards, tortoises and snakes, reproduce on land and can survive in areas with very little water.

The Komodo dragon *can weigh up to 150 kilogrammes and grow to a length of 3 metres*

Fish out of water

African lungfishes can survive even when the rivers run dry. They burrow into mud and hide in a cocoon until the rivers rise again.

Dangerous – or in danger?

Here you can see crocodiles, venomous snakes and poisonous frogs. Even the Komodo dragon, the largest living lizard, has been known to attack people, but some species are themselves in danger, as confirmed by the crocodile handbag on show.

Marine Invertebrates

13

Life Galleries

(30 minutes) Ground floor

Listen to the sea as it splashes gently on the shore while you browse over the hundreds of colourful sea creatures displayed in traditional cases. Don't forget to look up at the life-size, 18-metre model of a giant squid, the largest animal without a backbone.

Sea animals without backbones are divided into many different groups. Sponges, whose skeletons are built by millions of single-celled animals, have lived in every ocean for 600 million years, making them far older than dinosaurs. Molluscs often have beautiful shells (view the stunning Karo collection) and crustaceans are in fact arthropods – see them in the *Creepy-crawlies* exhibition too. Marine conservation is crucial to protect all these creatures from commercial exploitation.

Did you know?

Pearls originate as foreign particles that became trapped in oyster shells and encased in mother of pearl; look out for a fish which became a pearl. Parasitic round-worms can be up to eight metres long. All echinoderms (sea urchins, starfish and sea cucumbers) have a five-rayed body plan, and are brightly coloured when alive. Cephalopods such as squid and octopus swim by squirting water out through their siphon.

Taking advantage

Discover how humans harvest many marine invertebrates for food, ornaments and medicine; and learn how HM Customs have to be vigilant in their work to confiscate specimens from the smugglers, who threaten marine invertebrates and their habitats.

The model of a giant squid spans the gallery

Dinosaurs

21

Life
Galleries

(30–40 minutes)
Ground floor

Experience the thrilling drama of life amongst the dinosaurs. Modern robotic technology allows you to witness history as a roaring, breathing* Tyrannosaurus rex *feeds on a freshly killed* Tenontosaurus *at the end of the walkway.

Dinosaurs lived on Earth for about 160 million years, but became extinct 65 million years ago – 61 million years before the first humans appeared. They were a hugely varied group of reptiles, which lived on land, could not fly and walked on straight legs tucked underneath their bodies. Our knowledge about these creatures is gained through the painstaking detective work of palaeontologists who examine their fossilized remains and compare them with animals alive today. We have learnt how the skeletons of today's animals reflect their lifestyles and we can apply this understanding to the fossil clues left by dinosaurs. Fossils of bones and teeth, eggs or rarely even skin, continue to be found in rocks all over the world and astonishing new species are still being discovered.

A walkover

A 70 – metre raised walkway takes you past a huge variety of dinosaur skeletons and models. Imagine what a fearsome hunter *Deinocheirus* (or 'terrible hand') must have been when you see its massive arm and shoulder bones, and marvel at the amazing eight – metre length of Iguanodon.

More than a sting in the tail

Most dinosaurs were vegetarians and so to defend themselves from meateaters like *Tyrannosaurus*, some developed highly effective armour. Fossils in the exhibition show that *Euoplocephalus* had armour plating and a huge, heavy and offensive club at the end of its tail.

A fearsome predator, Tyrannosaurus rex

What happened to them?

Was there a change of climate, or did a meteorite strike the Earth? There are many theories, some bizarre, as to why dinosaurs became extinct suddenly about 65 million years ago. The exhibition explores some ideas – perhaps you have your own theory.

Reconstruction of Orodromeus *nest found in Montana, USA*

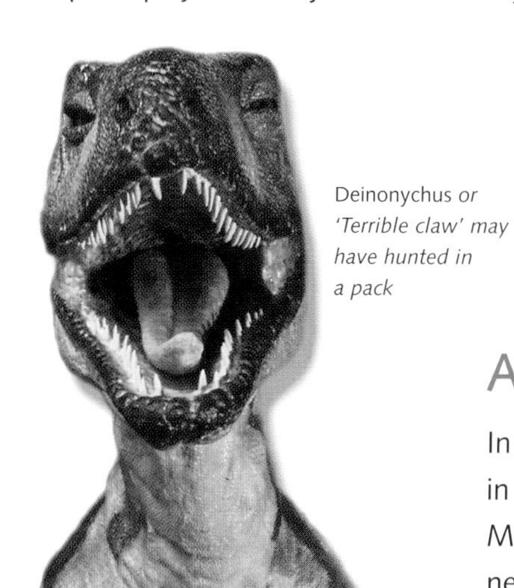

Deinonychus *or 'Terrible claw' may have hunted in a pack*

Ancient claw

In 1983 William Walker discovered an enormous claw bone in a Surrey claypit. Palaeontologists from The Natural History Museum excavated the site and uncovered the remains of a new dinosaur which they called *Baryonyx walkeri*. Learn more about 'Claws', as it has been nicknamed, from the exhibit that shows how the Museum built up this dinosaur's appearance and lifestyle from its fossilized remains.

Human biology

22

Life
Galleries

(30–40 minutes)
Ground floor

Take a really close look at yourself, and discover just how amazing you are. This highly interactive exhibition gives you the chance to marvel at, and test your mind and body, and understand their growth and development.

Each of us begins life as a single tiny cell, but by the time we are born, our bodies consist of millions of cells.
Our brains control most of our actions, through nerves and the action of hormones, the body's chemical messengers. Sometimes these actions are in response to information gathered from the outside world through our sense organs and nervous system. Sometimes we respond to messages sent from within the body in order to maintain conditions such as temperature or oxygen and water content.
These control systems allow us to take so much for granted: our senses, growth, digestion, respiration and temperature regulation.

Growing up

Visit the giant model of an unborn baby, and experience, as you once did yourself, the soothing and powerful sounds that a baby hears within the womb. Play the *Imposters* game to understand how physical characteristics are inherited.

Jogging your memory

How good is your memory? How do you remember people's names? Could you recognize an armed raider if you saw the person again in a police identity parade? Find out about the different kinds of memory we use for different purposes, and how we learn and remember.

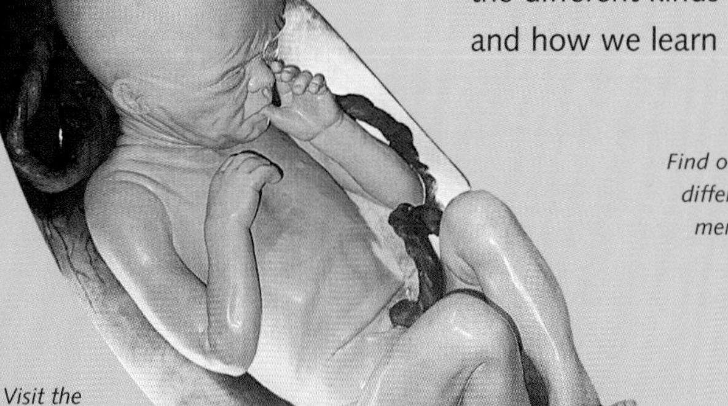

Visit the giant model of an unborn baby

Find out about the different kinds of memory we use

Imagine what a Martian might learn from human beings

This shows how you would look if each part of your body grew in proportion to the area of the brain responsible for its movement

What a sight

Test your ability to perceive information through your eyes. Optical illusions and other exhibits will allow you to experience how your prior knowledge or expectation can affect what you see, and how you learn to judge distances and widths.

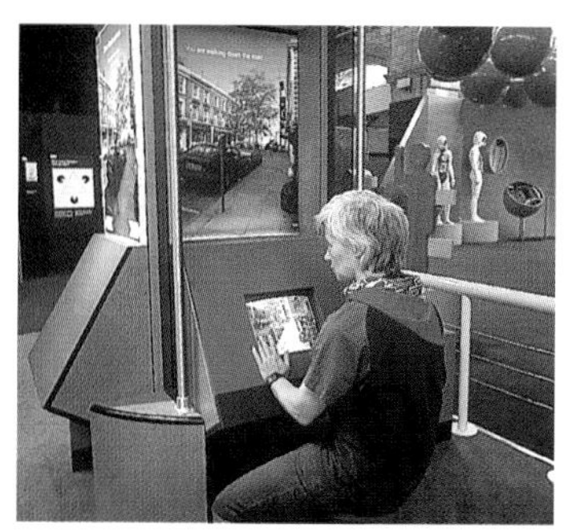

Test yourself. Could you recognise an armed raider if you saw the person again?

You're never too old

As soon as we are born, we begin to learn about our surroundings. This learning process continues throughout our lives, as we use our memories to store what we have discovered so that we can solve ever more complex problems to make sense of our world.

Mammals

23/24

Life
Galleries

(30–40 minutes)
Ground floor

Imagine that you are in the ocean, watching the largest creature ever to have lived swimming above you. The awesome life-size model of a blue whale, suspended from the gallery ceiling, dwarfs even the largest of the modern mammals and their fossil relatives in this two-level exhibition

While not as numerous as arthropods, mammals exist in amazing variety – from the magnificent polar bear to the tiny pigmy shrew. Scientists trace the path of mammal evolution, and the exhibition contains fossils and skeletons of extinct animals such as *Smilodon*, a sabre-toothed cat that lived about 15,000 years ago. Mammals have long been the inspiration for myths and legends: the sirenians, or sea cows, were mistaken for mermaids by early sailors, and the narwhal's impressive spiral tusks inspired tales of unicorns.

Adaptable artiodactyls

Artiodactyls are the largest group of hoofed mammals, and include camels, deer, goats and hippopotamuses. They are extremely well-adapted to their environments. Camels, for example, have extraordinary systems for conserving water; compare their bodily functions with those of cows in this exhibit.

Discover why

The *Massive mammals* interactive displays show what supports the enormous weight of a whale. Find out if elephants can jump, how their legs differ from horses' legs and why they have big ears.

The deep blue sea

Displayed on the balcony are the cetaceans: mammals that spend their lives in the sea. Discover how they breathe: listen to whale songs and dolphin clicks; marvel at how dolphins learn our language; and learn how all these creatures maintain their depth in the water using stores of oils and waxes in their heads.

Cetaceans like the common porpoise are mammals that spend their lives in the sea

This magnificent polar bear stands 1.5 metres tall

The awesome model of a blue whale is suspended from the gallery ceiling

Stranded

A poignant video features cetaceans that have become stranded on shores, where they often die, despite human attempts to rescue them. The Natural History Museum keeps a register of all reported strandings on British shores, so that scientists can find out more about them.

The Jerwood Gallery

26

Life
Galleries

(30 minutes)
Ground floor

Restored to its original splendour, revealing the Alfred Waterhouse terracotta, triple-arched opening and high level stained glass windows for the first time since it was badly damaged in World War 11, the* Jerwood Gallery *was inaugurated in September 1999.

A stunning new venue, the *Jerwood Gallery* will host an exciting programme of art exhibitions. Rarely seen treasures fromthe Museum's unrivalled collection of natural history art (the third largest collection of art on paper in the UK) will be revealed, often for the first time and contemporary artistic expression will explore topical natural science issues.

This vibrant new space will also host an exhibition of images from the biggest and most prestigious wildlife photography competition in the world, the BG Wildlife Photographer of the Year exhibition - a joint venture between The Natural History Museum and BBC Wildlife Magazine.

For details of forthcoming exhibitions in the *Jerwood Gallery*, please call 020 7942 5067.

The restoration of the *Jerwood Gallery* has been made possible by the generous support of the Jerwood Foundation.

Fossil marine reptiles

30

Life
Galleries

(20 minutes)
Ground floor

As you stroll down Waterhouse Way, stop and look at some of the finest fossil marine reptiles ever found in Britain – many discovered by a very determined Victorian lady.

While dinosaurs roamed the land, very different reptiles inhabited the seas. These marine reptiles included ichthyosaurs and plesiosaurs that lived 220 to 65 million years ago. Today, their closest surviving relatives are lizards and snakes. Some of the finest specimens in Waterhouse Way were unearthed in Dorset by Mary Anning (1799–1847). She was only 11 years old when she discovered a complete ichthyosaur skeleton, and remained a passionate fossil hunter for the rest of her life.

This pregnant female Ichthyosaur lived 187–178 million years ago and was found at Baden-Wurthenberg in Germany

Different types of ammonite discovered in Jurassic rocks near Lyme Regis in Dorset

Fossils from Britain

Much of the rock that covers Britain is formed from layers of small rock fragments that have been squeezed together over millions of years. During this process, the remains of plants and animals became buried in the layers, creating a fossil record of Britain's past. *Fossils from Britain* is in **Gallery 31**.

Ecology

32

Life
Galleries

(30–40 minutes)
Ground floor

Discover how we are linked with all the other living things in our world, a complex environment where the balance of the essential ingredients of life – air, earth, energy from sunlight and water – is crucial to survival.

Ecology is the study of connections. It examines the links between all Earth's diverse life-forms, communities and environments, and the changes that can lead to new life, or to destruction. Humans are just one piece in this complex jigsaw, which is constantly changing as natural disasters, human activity and shifts in climate influence growth and decline.

Follow the water cycle

This vast and spectacular video wall shows how water vapour rises from the oceans to form clouds, which pour rain onto the land. Animals and plants take in the life-giving liquid and rivers carry it, laden with nutrients, back downstream to the oceans.

The struggle for energy

The energy for all life comes from the sun. Sunlight, deadly until filtered by the Earth's atmosphere, is used by plants to produce carbohydrates. Using a rabbit as an example, an exhibit demonstrates, how herbivores absorb energy by eating plants before, in turn, being eaten by carnivores. When carnivores are eaten by other carnivores, or die and are broken down into the raw materials of life by scavengers and fungi, the process of recycling continues.

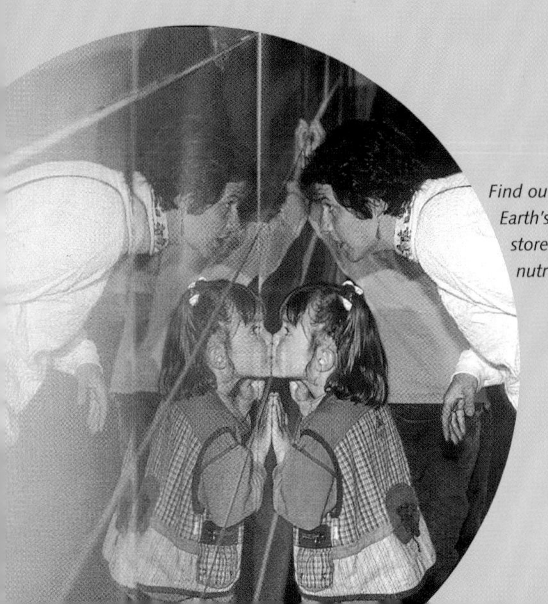

Find out how the Earth's lithosphere stores essential nutrients for life

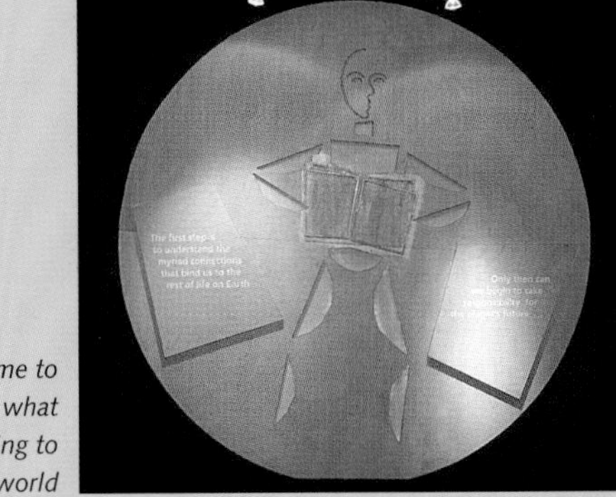

Take time to think about what we are doing to our world

Follow the water cycle on the spectacular video wall

Giant leaf

Step into the leaf factory and discover how energy from the sun is used to convert carbon dioxide into carbohydrates. Standing, one eight-thousandth of your normal size, amongst the cells of a gigantic leaf, you will see how the process of photosynthesis provides a waste product, oxygen, on which all life depends.

The leaf factory illustrates the process of photosynthesis

What are we doing?

Human beings are causing dramatic and destructive changes to the Earth, with little regard for the value of the life-forms they have forced to the brink of extinction. The huge 'green man' sculpture at the end of the exhibition is a symbol of our responsibility to work with the Earth and its ecology, not against it, in the future.

Ecology *is sponsored by British Petroleum.*

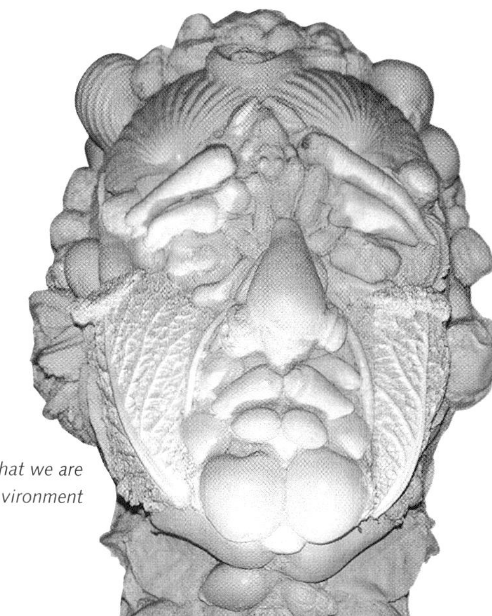

The 'green man' reminds us that we are part of our environment

33

Creepy crawlies

Life
Galleries

(30 minutes)
Ground floor

Watch closely as thousands of live fungus-growing ants work to produce their own food. Then pay a visit to No. 1 Crawley House, to see just how close our relationship is with some of the other members of the vast arthropod group.

So far, around 1.3 million different kinds of arthropod are known. Many, many more remain to be discovered. The group includes insects, spiders, crustaceans and centipedes. From microscopic mites to giant spider crabs, their success is due to their adaptability – living in the air, soil or water, they may eat anything from wood to flower heads, and paper to nectar; and defend themselves through camouflage, armour or weaponry; or a mix of all three. Some arthropods are harmful to humans: the mosquito, for instance, may pass on disease, and some species of scorpion have a potentially deadly sting. Many more are important to the environment; there is, for example, a large community of soil arthropods that help to enrich the soil and many insects, such as bees, pollinate plants.

Varied diet

The exhibition's 'vending machine' shows examples of the enormous variety of diets enjoyed by arthropods. Dishes on offer include dung, bacon and seaweed, and you are welcome to make your own selections.

Time for a change

The *Changes* exhibit demonstrates how young arthropods become adults in some fascinating ways. All arthropods' skeletons are on the outside and they shed and replace them as they grow. All, too, begin their life cycles as eggs. Some develop into caterpillars and then change into butterflies and moths in a process known as metamorphosis.

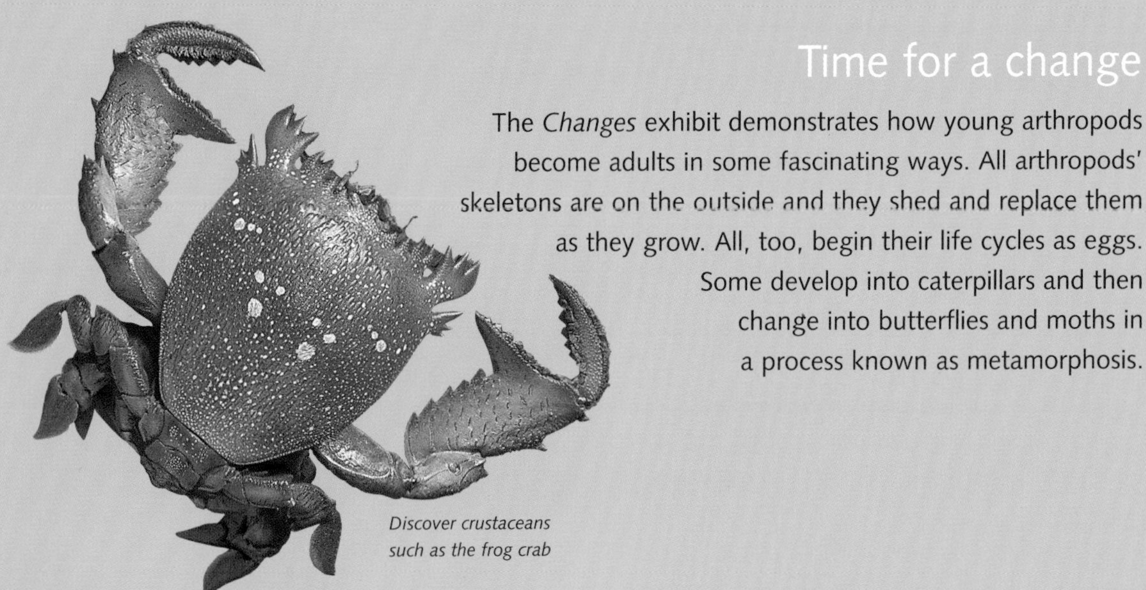

Discover crustaceans such as the frog crab

Technical masterpiece

The enormous tower in the centre of the exhibition is a replica of the largest structure built by arthropods. Sometimes reaching over five metres in height, the termite mound is an astounding feat of engineering, built by millions of tiny, blind insects to ensure that their highly organized underground cities remain fully ventilated and at a constant temperature.

Learn about the arthropod group, which represents 80 per cent of all animals

Close encounters

Visit No. 1 Crawley House, where you can see just how many arthropods might share your home. You may be surprised by their number and variety, particularly in your kitchen.

Have a close encounter with this gigantic moving model of a scorpion

Birds

Life
Galleries

(15 minutes)
Ground floor

Imagine going back to 1881, when The Natural History Museum first opened. Some of the display cases in this exhibition remain as they were then, giving us a fascinating insight into the history of biology.

This exhibition shows, in minute detail, the variety, behaviour, anatomy and nesting habits of many different species. It also presents a unique opportunity to see how the museum has developed. Many of the original bird exhibits were destroyed by bombs during the Second World War, those that remain can now be seen alongside newly created exhibits.

The flightless dodo, native of Mauritius, became extinct in the seventeenth century

A clutch of eggs

A hummingbird egg is about the size of a cherry stone, but is large in proportion to the size of the bird that laid it. At the other end of the scale, the enormous ostrich egg is very small in comparison with the full-sized bird.

Exotic antique

A beautiful display of exotic hummingbirds, with their nests and eggs, is a typical example of the kind of case that was popular in Victorian times. This is a wonderful opportunity to see at close quarters the gorgeous colours of the birds' plumage.

Lasting impressions

50

Life
Galleries

(15–20 minutes)
Ground floor

Find out how the ripples of waves on a sandy beach have lasted 200 million years; see rocks that grow from the outside in; and discover how you can tell a whale's age from its teeth. Mark your passage between the Life Galleries and the Earth Galleries by seeing at very close quarters, some amazing objects that have recorded elements of their own history.

In our world, the passage of time is marked by growth and change. Each object displayed in this gallery has, clear evidence of its age or an event in its past, captured forever within its structure.

Rusty coral

Examine the red line that runs right through a cut piece of coral. The coral has absorbed the colour produced by iron pollution, which at some time affected the sea it inhabited, so recording the event forever.

Growing old slowly

Arctic lichens increase in diameter by as little as one millimetre in 50 years and can live for up to 10,000 years. This knowledge has enabled scientists to estimate the age of the giant stone figures on South Pacific's Easter Island.

Examine objects that have recorded elements of their history

Mollusc shells grow in bands that are sometimes annual, and sometimes triggered by climatic events

Our place in evolution

101

Life
Galleries

(15–20 minutes)
First floor

Learn how much we have in common with creatures that walked the Earth millions of years ago, by exploring the four sections of this exhibition.

Compare modern human skulls with those of our living and fossil relatives

Scientists have discovered which members of the ape family are our closest living relatives, by comparing features that share the same structure, such as bones, teeth and chromosomes. However, apes and monkeys alive today do not walk upright as we do, and have smaller brains. Scientists apply similar techniques to fossils, to find primates that were even more closely related to us. Our closer fossil relatives walked on two legs, made tools and used fire.

Learning from Lucy

Lucy was an australopithecine who lived in Africa about three million years ago. Examine the reconstruction of this female, and the footprints that show that her species walked upright.

Funeral fire

The remains of a Neanderthal child, found in a narrow pit surrounded by goats' horns and with evidence of a fire beside it, have suggested to some scientists that these large-brained people, who lived in Europe and the Middle East between 150,000 and 40,000 years ago, may have buried their dead, as we do.

Find out what an australopithecine who lived three million years ago looked like

Minerals

Life
Galleries

(30 minutes)
First floor

Enjoy the rare privilege of exploring an enormous and comprehensive classified research display of over 3,000 minerals, and discover why toothpaste, matches and a stainless steel teapot have a place here too.

The Minerals *gallery*

Rocks are composed of minerals, without which life on Earth would be impossible. This immense scientific collection of minerals is displayed according to chemical composition and structure. It includes gemstones, that have been cut and polished to reveal their beauty.

Everyday examples

Explore the many ways in which we use minerals in our everyday lives. Diamonds, for example, are a symbol of love and beauty in jewellery, but they are also the hardest minerals on Earth and therefore have many industrial uses.

Heat treatment

Examine radioactive minerals displayed safely in a specially designed unit. Marvel at the distorted nails, coins and glass fused by the heat of a volcanic eruption – a taster for your visit to *The power within*.

See a model of the largest nugget of gold ever found in Australia

Meteorites

103

Life
Galleries

(15 minutes)
First floor

Discover the origin of shooting stars and huge craters in the Earth's surface. The Natural History Museum has pieces of many of the 10,000 to 15,000 meteorites that have been recovered after they fell to Earth from space.

Fragments of rock from asteroids are constantly bombarding the Earth, but most are only the size of dust particles. Shooting stars are the tiniest meteors; pieces of dust that burn up completely in the atmosphere. The fragments that reach the Earth's surface are known as meteorites, and can be enormous. Composed of iron, stone, or a mixture of the two, meteorites are distinct from tektites, which are the glassy objects formed during the impact of a meteorite into the Earth's surface. Tektites are terrestrial rocks transformed during an extraterrestrial event.

Heavy shower

Housed at the far end of *Minerals*, the Cranbourne is a 3.5-tonne iron meteorite, the largest of at least 11 enormous boulders that fell over Victoria, Australia some time before 1854. Trace the landing pattern of the meteorite shower on a map of the area, and imagine what a sight it must have been.

Star gazing

The study of meteorites gives scientists valuable clues about the history of the Earth, the sun and our entire solar system. Because meteorites are samples of objects from space, where few people have the chance to go, they have often been called 'the poor man's space probe'.

Close encounters of the meteorite kind

Plant power

108

The Plant power *exhibition examines the interaction between plants and people*

Life Galleries

(15–20 minutes)
First floor

We cannot live without them, but we take them for granted. View plants from a very different perspective in this photographic exhibition, which examines some fundamental, and sometimes deeply uncomfortable, truths about our relationship with the plant kingdom.

The interaction between plants and people is constant and essential. From cosmetics to cars, and from staple foods to slavery, plants have played a crucial part in mankind's economic, cultural and social development. Photographs of 18 different plants and their products are displayed. The images, combined with quotations from literature, cosmetic catalogues, speeches and recipes, explore moral issues surrounding our dependence on plants.

Cotton candy

Learn how, for three centuries of our history, people exploited their fellow humans in the name of two vital plant crops. Sugar cultivation in Africa during the seventeenth and eighteenth centuries, and cotton production in nineteenth century America were supported by ruthless slavery.

Food and fertility

The yam is a staple food in Southeast Asia. In 1942, a Mexican species was used to produce progesterone, leading to the development of the contraceptive pill. This has had a profound effect on sexual and social behaviour in the West, and the collage of images may prompt you to consider the benefits and dangers of this control over human fertility.

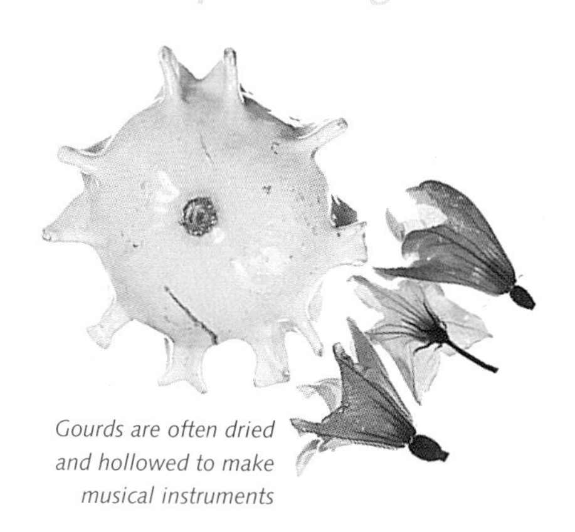

Gourds are often dried and hollowed to make musical instruments

Primates

107

Life
Galleries

(20 minutes)
First floor

Visit our close relatives, the primates, and discover the differences and the amazing similarities between us.
Exhibits on the west balcony overlooking the Central hall show the intelligence, communication and social behaviour of primates, and remind us of the dangers they face.

Gibbon skeletons swing across the ceiling

We, *Homo sapiens*, are the most widespread and successful primates in the world today. Like us, bush-babies, lorises, lemurs, apes and monkeys have 3D vision and some also have an opposable thumb and finger with which to grasp objects. Apes are among the most intelligent of all mammals; some make use of tools, a skill that requires foresight and dexterity, while others discover new ways of doing things, which they are able to communicate to their group, adding to their culture (much as humans do). Apes can even learn symbols that represent objects, and some scientists believe they can 'talk' with them.

Sculpture and skeletons

At the entrance to the exhibition is a dramatic wire mesh sculpture, which evokes the relationship between us and the other primates. Amongst the different exhibits, under gibbon skeletons that swing from the ceiling, are bronze sculptures that portray aggression, intimacy, play and the bonding of mother and offspring in the primate world. You may recognize similarities to human behaviour.

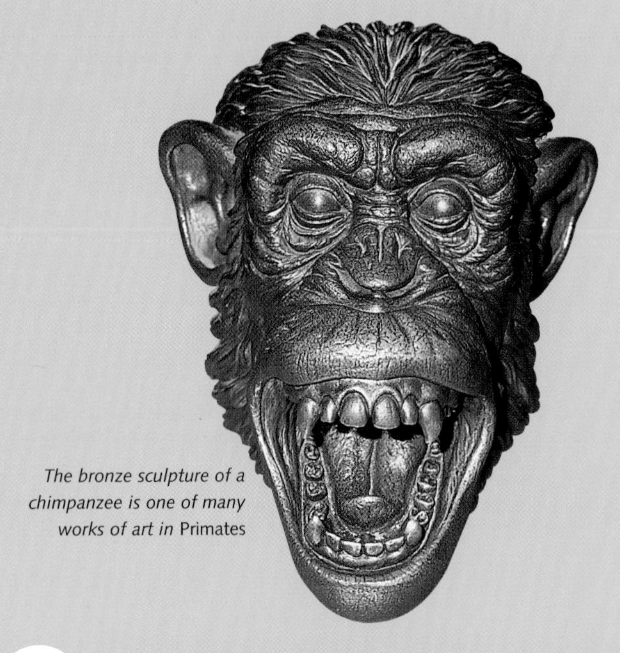

The bronze sculpture of a chimpanzee is one of many works of art in Primates

The Primates *gallery*

Skillful sifting

Japanese macaques demonstrate the considerable intelligence of primates in their solution to the problem of sifting rice grains from sand. Discover how they use water to separate the grains.

Deceitful baboons

Use the interactive display to learn how a female baboon can groom a low-status male without provoking the jealous anger of a dominant male, by using her intelligence and awareness of perspective to deceive him.

Under threat

Over half of all primate species are threatened by hunting and deforestation. Learn how the giant lemur became extinct in Madagascar 2,000 years ago, and how 12 other species of lemur have died out since the arrival of their human relatives. Discover, here and in the *Ecology* exhibition, the importance of conservation.

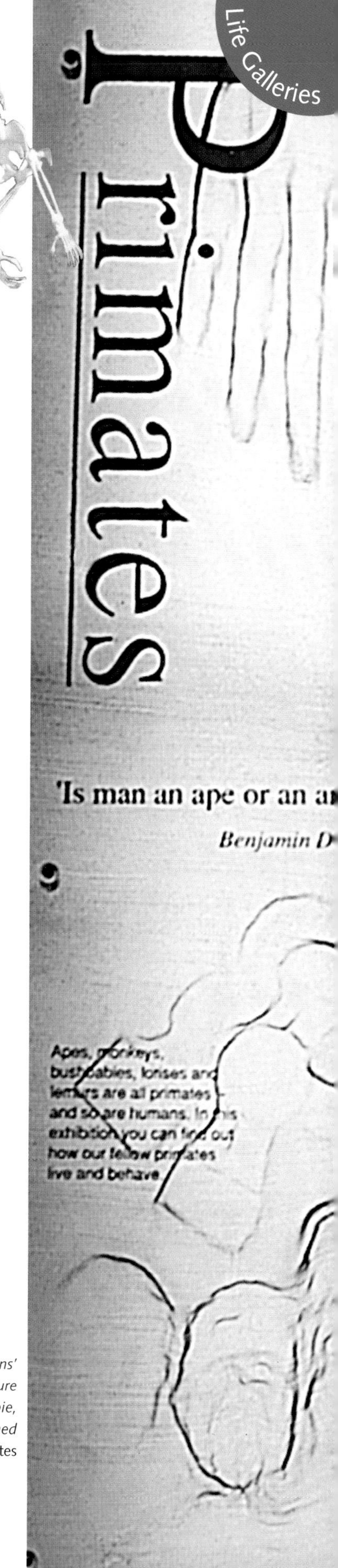

Part of 'Origins' a sculpture by David Begbie, commissioned for Primates

105

Origin of species

Life
Galleries

(30–40 minutes)
Ground floor

Follow the steps of Charles Darwin's theory of natural selection, and decide whether you agree with his explanation for the enormous number of different species that live on Earth.

Darwin spent years travelling around the world, collecting specimens and investigating the breeding of plants and animals, before publishing *On the Origin of Species by Means of Natural Selection* in 1859. In it, he observed that all species have the potential to produce more than enough offspring to replace themselves; but their environments present dangers that limit the number of offspring able to survive. Species that are better suited to the environment are more likely to live and breed themselves, so passing their characteristics to their own offspring. Over generations, the proportion of individuals with beneficial characteristics is likely to increase.

Artificial selection

Dog breeders mimic natural selection to produce dogs with specific features. They choose individuals with those features (such as large size, great strength or the ability to hunt by scent) and breed them over many generations. Understand more of Darwin's argument by observing the display of dogs resulting from this process.

Natural selection

Play *The natural selection game* to find out how Darwin's theory works in practice. Mice with dark fur are more likely to survive than those with pale fur, because they are less visible to predatory owls. Since more dark mice survive to reproduce, there will eventually be a greater proportion of dark mice in the population.

Darwin's theory attempted to explain why there are so many different species on Earth

Charles Darwin 1809–1882

Introducing genetics

Darwin did not know about the mechanism of genetics. Although he realized that characteristics were inherited he did not know how. Now that we understand the role of genes and chromosomes in inheritance we can see how natural selection operates in the process of evolution.

A strange case

People who suffer from the inherited disease known as sickle cell anaemia demonstrate a quirk of natural selection. Since most sufferers do not survive to reproduce, the disease should die out. However, people carrying the sickle cell gene are more resistant to mosquito-borne malaria than those without it, giving them a higher chance of survival.

Discover how genes can mutate when copying their instructions

Rowland Ward pavilion

African mammals

106

Life
Galleries

(15 minutes)
First floor

Take the opportunity to see this extraordinary collection of African animals in a reconstruction of their natural habitat. This is a place in which you can see how different animal groups shown elsewhere in the Museum actually live together.

The giraffe has to bend awkwardly on its long legs to drink at this Kenyan waterhole

Located behind *Origin of species*, this pavilion houses three dioramas showing scenes from different African environments, and the animals which populate them.

Keeping a look-out

The sable antelope, using the top of a termite colony as a look-out, is a feature of the Angolan landscape.
The giraffe, the tallest living land mammal, needs no such vantage point, but is nevertheless vulnerable to predators; it has to bend awkwardly on its long legs to drink.

Living together

Here arthropods, mammals and birds are all represented in a single scene. The red-billed oxpecker has a mutually beneficial relationship with large mammals; it picks out and eats the ticks, flies and other parasites that live on them.

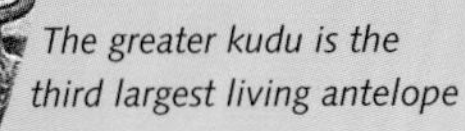

The greater kudu is the third largest living antelope

Investigate

B2

Life
Galleries

(30-40 minutes)
The Clore Education Centre (Basement)

Designed with 7–14 year olds (and their adult companions) in mind, Investigate *is a new kind of exhibition that combines hundreds of objects from the natural world with some of the tools that scientists use to explore them.*

The scientists at The Natural History Museum have discovered a great deal about the natural world, in *Investigate* you can share the excitement they feel when exploring new objects by making your own discoveries using many of the tools scientists use. Take a look at hundreds of specimens, large and small, and select the ones you want to investigate. You'll find magnifying and measuring tools at a nearby workstation to help you study your selections more closely. Questions on the wall, on 'Qcards' and in the workstation computer will give you more ideas to investigate. *The courtyard garden* and the *live area* give you a chance to explore living organisms and discover how the seasons affect nature and at the *information centre* you can find out more about natural history discoveries making the news.
The communications centre offers virtual objects to explore and a chance to share your own discoveries on the web. Each month there's a different activity to try and, if you like puzzles, you can try some of the 'jigsaw' activities on the *sticky wall*.

Investigate is an invaluable resource for schools and admission is set aside for school visits during term weekday mornings. Other visitors are welcome from Tuesday to Friday between 14.30 and 17.00hrs during term and from Monday to Friday between 10.30 and 17.00 in school holidays. At weekends *Investigate* is open between 10.30 and 17.00 on Saturdays and 11.30 and 17.00 on Sundays.
Investigate is in the Clore Education Centre which is supported by The Vivien Duffield Foundation.

Visions of Earth

60

Earth
Galleries

(20 minutes)
Ground floor

Your dramatic introduction to the Earth Galleries is a massive sculpture of the Earth itself, suspended high above you, around one of the longest escalators in Europe. Walk down the avenue of sculptures that leads to it, and examine stunningly beautiful specimens through windows in the etched slate walls of the gallery.

The Earth sciences explore our planet's place in the universe, the materials it is made of, the changes it undergoes and the effect that we have on it. The iron, zinc and copper globe, which dominates the gallery, symbolizes the many layers of atmosphere, crust and core that make up the Earth. It is enveloped by towering slate walls etched with the constellations of the night sky, and the planets of our solar system, so showing us our place in the universe.
The escalator, which runs straight through the globe, leads to the top floor of the Earth Galleries.

Saltpetre, sulphur and charcoal, first combined by the ancient Chinese to make firecrackers. This explosive mixture dramatically influenced the history of warfare

Discover the truth behind the myth of the one-eyed Cyclops

Take the escalator on a journey through the sculptured iron, zinc and copper globe

Bronze icons

Six imposing statues highlight key issues in our understanding of the Earth. Discover the truth behind the myth of the one-eyed Cyclops; learn how the ancients believed that the Earth was the centre of the universe; and consider how we can take care of our planet while still using its resources.

The same, but different

Graphite, the soft material which is sometimes used as the 'lead' in pencils, is chemically identical to diamond, the hardest known substance. Find these polymorphs, as they are known, in one of the specimen windows that line the gallery.

Moon rock

Enjoy a rare opportunity to see a piece of the moon! This rock is part of a sample brought to Earth by the astronauts of the *Apollo 16* mission, which landed on the moon in 1972.

Pillar pattern

Find the inspiration behind the pillar decorations in the Life Galleries. The fossil leaf scars from the bark of *Lepidodendron* form the beautiful regular pattern that Alfred Waterhouse used in his design for the Museum.

The Natural History Museum gratefully acknowledges the support of the National Lottery through the Heritage Lottery Fund, and Rio Tinto plc in the development of the Earth Galleries exhibitions.

The power within

61

Earth
Galleries

(30–40 minutes)
Second floor

Find out how an earthquake feels, and what happens when a volcano erupts. Check for yourself where there have been earthquakes in the last week, and discover how scientists can predict where and when the next ones might be.

The effects of the massive natural forces that stem from within the Earth are experienced, often violently, at the surface. By studying these effects, scientists can discover more about our world, and predict when earthquakes or eruptions might occur.

The vast slabs, known as tectonic plates, which make up the Earth's crust are in constant motion, and over millions of years they collide, move apart or slide over each other, sometimes with devastating results. Evidence of this includes the discovery of marine fossils in the Himalayas, suggesting that 50 million years ago the world's highest mountain range was part of the ocean floor.

Under the volcano

Witness terrifying video images of volcanic activity, and watch a reconstruction of the events surrounding the 1991 eruption of Mount Pinatubo, when clouds of ash blotted out the sun. Hundreds died in this disaster, but volcanologists were able to save thousands more by their close monitoring of the volcano, and their accurate predictions of its eruption.

A moment in history

The famous eruption of Mount Vesuvius in AD 79 destroyed the town of Pompeii, but ironically preserved the remains of it and its inhabitants for future generations to study and learn from. You can see reconstructions of the casts, made in the hardened ash, of a man and a dog who died there.

View terrifying images of volcanic eruption

Supermarket shake-up

Stand in a Japanese supermarket and experience a simulation of the terrible earthquake that killed 6,000 people in the city of Kobe in 1995. This display is dedicated to the memory of those who died.

Learning from experience

Examine the different methods, both ancient and modern, which have been used to predict earthquakes and learn how engineers are designing quake-proof technology for buildings as a safeguard for the future.

Find out where there have been earthquakes in the past week

Understand the different methods used to predict earthquakes

Experience an earthquake as you stand in the reconstruction of a Japanese supermarket

Restless surface

62

Earth
Galleries

(30–40 minutes)
Second florr

Learn about the forces that move mountains, polish rocks, change the direction of rivers, turn sand into glass and alter the Earth's climate. Discover why the surface of our world is constantly reshaping, while the moon is still and lifeless.

Since the Earth's formation over four billion years ago, the landscape has been sculpted over and over again by wind, water, ice, heat and living things. Our world is always changing; some changes are instant, like a landslide, while others, such as the formation of coal from the decayed remains of ancient forests, take millions of years. When the continents of India and Asia met millions of years ago, the collision formed the Himalayas. The towering heights of this mountain range probably caused the climatic changes responsible for the last ice age, indicating the interplay between the internal and external forces acting on the Earth's surface.

Solid lightning

Find out how a flash of forked lightning hit desert sand and changed it instantly into a fulgurite, a hollow tube of glass.

Moving around

Wind, water and ice can move pieces of rock immense distances: ancient Scandinavian boulders were carried to Yorkshire (where they still stand) during the last ice age, and dust from central Asia has been found 11,000 kilometres away in Hawaii. Examine a sequence of stones, starting with a rough, jagged piece and ending with a smooth, round one: the smoother the stone, the further it is likely to have travelled.

How much energy does it take to create an air or water flow?

Settled material rarely remains undisturbed. This rock formed when soft red mud shrank and cracked in the sun. A darker sediment settled in the cracks and the whole hardened

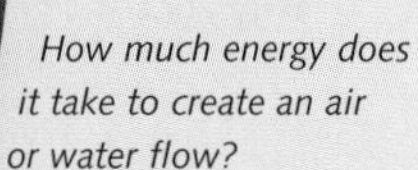

Discover how the Himalayas were formed

Examine a stalagmite, formed over hundreds of years from water depositing minerals as it dripped onto the floor of a cave

Major breakdown

When rainwater combines with carbon dioxide in the atmosphere, an acid solution is formed, which eats away at the stone it falls on. This affects buildings as well as the natural landscape. See how living things such as lichens also produce rock-attacking acids, and learn how plant roots affect rock too.

Winds, water, ice and life itself shape the land. All are part of the inevitable process of change

Rock of ages

Before you leave, see, in one magnificent rock specimen, a whole history of change at the Earth's surface. In it is recorded sediment formation, earth movements and crystal growth over tens of millions of years.

From the beginning

63

Earth
Galleries

(30–40 minutes)
First floor

Travel 20,000 million years, from the birth of the universe to the end of our solar system. A clever trick of perspective makes time appear to stretch far into the distance, where a crystal ball shows the future of the Earth.

The 'big bang' signalled the beginning of time about 15,000 million years ago. A resulting cloud of dust and gas formed our solar system 4,500 million years ago. This exhibition draws a comparison between the life of the solar system and a twelve-hour clock. Using the idea that now is midnight, we can see that multicellular organisms emerged after 10 o'clock, and human beings evolved just 20 seconds ago. Earth scientists have studied rocks and fossils to discover that the vastness of time has involved a turbulent history of moving continents, changing climate and mass extinctions, and the majority of species that have ever lived on Earth are now extinct.

Marking time

An engraved stainless steel time rail runs the length of the gallery, marking 25 million years with your every stride, while above, a mural shows how the Earth's continents are constantly moving, separating and joining. Discover that South and North American mammals and birds differ enormously because South America was isolated from other continents for 60 million years.

Reading the fossils

Learn how earth scientists determine the age of rocks and fossils, and see what they tell us about changing climate and environment. Not only can you marvel at one of the oldest rocks on earth, but you can also view one of the highest – a rock from the top of Mount Everest, eight kilometres above sea level.

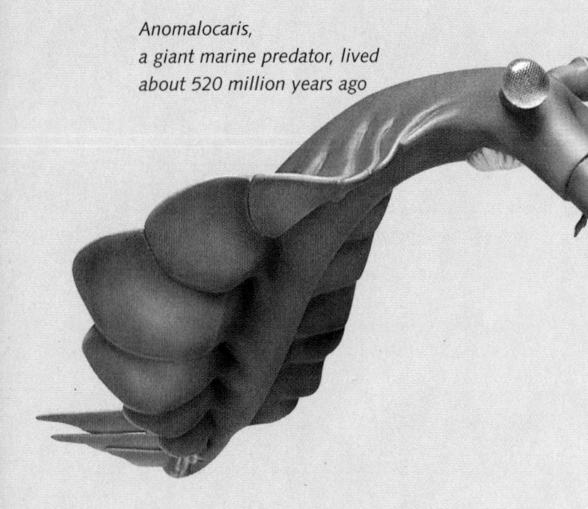

Anomalocaris, a giant marine predator, lived about 520 million years ago

A trick of perspective makes time appear to stretch far into the distance

How old is Britain?

Take a geological tour through Britain from the relatively young rocks in South East England to ancient rocks, over 3,000 million years old, in North West Scotland.

Earth underwent many dramatic changes before life began to evolve

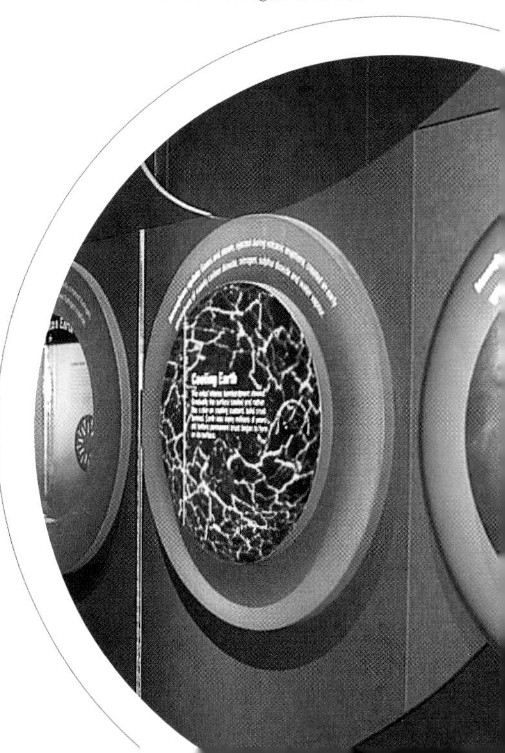

Death and disaster

Rising sea level, earthquakes and climate changes have all contributed to the five mass extinctions which have occurred since the Earth began. Find the probable reason for the devastating death of the dinosaurs, and witness the shadow that humanity has cast over other species living today. Human impact is not new – the sabre-toothed cat was probably hunted to extinction about 12,000 years ago.

What will you find in the geological tour suitcases?

Earth's treasury

64

Earth
Galleries

(30–40 minutes)
First floor

Take a rare opportunity to see some of the world's most precious treasures in a stunningly beautiful setting. Diamonds and gems are just the beginning of this story; you will discover that some of our more humble rocks and minerals have an even greater value today.

This peaceful, low-lit, glittering gallery is home to fine specimens of the thousands of gemstones, rocks and minerals on which so much of our existence depends. The geological processes that produce these treasures concentrate them in specific areas of the Earth's crust, and mineralogists can use their knowledge to help us to find them. Each rock and mineral has its own special properties, and its own value to us; the Museum's experts work on finding new and sophisticated applications for our existing resources, while also studying new minerals to predict their useful properties.

A thing of beauty

Diamond is simply a form of carbon - one of the most common elements – but because of its unique properties, it has huge significance and mystique. Gaze at the stunning display of rough diamonds, straight from the mine, and admire their brilliance when cut and polished.

Silica, an unexpected treasure, invaluable to our way of life

Innovative ideas

Our mineral resources have been developed in countless ways to provide everyday items we take for granted. Discover which minerals you are wearing in your spectacles, swallowing in your medicines or spending at the shops.

A beautiful specimen of Rhodochrosite from the U.S.A.

Chips with everything

Together silicon and oxygen form silica – known, in its crystalline state, as quartz. Discover how quartz keeps time so accurately, and how it is also used to make fire. Silica is also the raw material for silicon, a material infinitely precious to us. Silicon chips are at the heart of every computer, and most electronic equipment today. Where would we be without it?

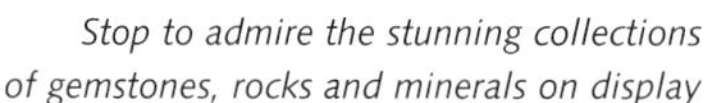

Stop to admire the stunning collections of gemstones, rocks and minerals on display

All in a grain of sand

When combined with other elements, silica forms silicates, the most common materials in the Earth's crust. But these everyday minerals, usually starting out as sand in rivers and on sea shores, are probably the most valuable of all. Find out about the building materials made from silicates; then look at the exhibits in this gallery, and consider how many you would have seen without glass!

This exhibition is supported by De Beers

65

Earth today & tomorrow

Earth
Galleries

(30–40 minutes)
Ground floor

High above this exhibition hang pallets containing the number of loaves of bread and cans of cola consumed in a year by an average UK family of four. A barcode reader will help you to discover just what you cost the Earth.

We have a direct impact on the complex interactions between land, air, water and living things on our planet. We cultivate the land, harvest the sea and consume fresh water. We mine and quarry raw materials, we build cities, produce waste and burn fuel for energy. Not only do earth scientists help us to solve the problems related to this intensive use of our resources and the safe disposal of our waste products, but they also try to prevent further problems by advising us on how to manage and safeguard the Earth for future generations.

A hole under the Museum

The Museum has drilled a 150-metre borehole into the chalk that lies deep below this building. Here engineers have tapped into the water which lies under London. This resource is now used within the Museum. See a section of that borehole, and learn of the discoveries Museum scientists have made.

Throwing it all away

What do we do with the things we discard? Earth scientists help us to find and extract the minerals we need for the products we use in daily life, but they also advise us on how to recycle and ultimately dispose of them.

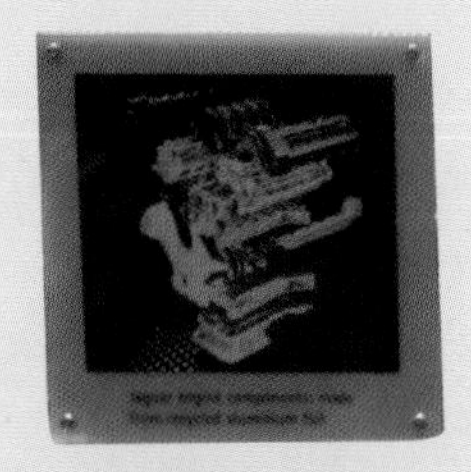

Find out how waste can sometimes be used as a resource

Scientists use borehole data to gain an understanding of what is happening underground

What went wrong with Biosphere 2?

We make our living spaces out of rocks and minerals mined from the Earth. Earth scientists advise us on how to minimize our use of these resources in building our cities and towns. Learn about the aims of the Biosphere 2 project, and the reason why, as an experiment in environmental management, it failed.

Running out

The gas and oil that cater for much of our energy demand are produced from the fossilized remains of living matter. These fossil fuels will eventually run out, and earth scientists are working to find alternatives, as well as improving the methods for detecting and improving the recovery of the fuel that still remains. Discover some alternative, renewable sources of energy illustrated by case studies from all over the world.

Engineering technologies allow building projects to take place on a massive scale

Scan the barcodes to find out what each product costs the Earth

66

Earth lab

Earth
Galleries

Mezzanine floor

Here is your chance to talk to earth scientists face-to-face, to examine rock and fossil specimens under the microscope, and to explore a database which can help you identify your own specimens.

The footprint of an Iguanadon

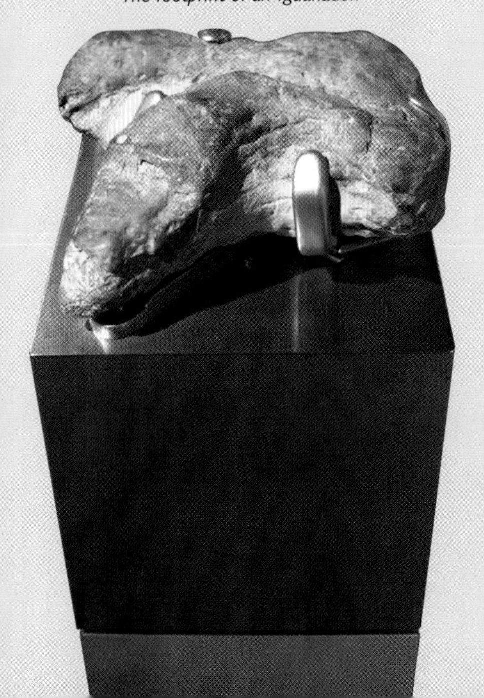

Earth lab is a resource for anyone wishing to delve deeper into the world of earth science. Scientists and explainers are on hand from 11.00 to 16.00 every day to assist and inspire children and adults alike. They will introduce you to a diverse collection of British rocks and fossils, and to the full records associated with each specimen, stored in a database which you can access through touch-screen computers. They will also welcome you into the lab, to sit at one of the fully-equipped workstations, and inspect specimens more closely.

Dinosaur footprint

As you enter *Earth lab*, you will see the astonishing cast of a footprint of an *Iguanadon* that lived in Hastings, England, 130 million years ago. Learn how the footprint was formed, and how it remained preserved for so long.

The truth behind the names

Find out about the processes that have created some very unusual rock formations, and see if you can identify these formations simply from their names. What, for example, do you think Hertfordshire Puddingstone looks like, and where would you find Hangman Grit and Dog-tooth Spar?

Bristol crocodile

Marvel at the display of wonderfully preserved British fossils, including crabs, lobsters and turtles, and use the computer to find out exactly how old they are. Don't miss the fossil crocodile that lived in the Bristol Channel between 159 and 180 million years ago.

Explore the database through touch-screen computers

Feel a fossil

Imagine the thrill of holding a fossil that is older than the dinosaurs. *Earth lab* scientists and explainers will offer you the chance to touch and examine at close range a collection of beautiful specimens that are hundreds of millions of years old.

In Earth lab *you can see a comprehensive display of British rocks, fossils and minerals*

Talk with scientists and examine your own rock and fossil specimens

Behind the scenes – *the collections*

The Natural History Museum is unique among Britain's national museums. Not only is it a major public attraction enjoyed by millions of visitors, but it is also a world-renowned institution for scientific research. These two functions support and enrich each other and are mostly carried out in the well – known and much loved Waterhouse building in South Kensington – itself a building of great architectural importance.

The Museum's vast collection, much of it unseen by the visiting public, forms an unrivalled database of life. More than 300 scientists and librarians work here, behind the scenes, researching, organizing and curating the collection of 68 million specimens and one million books and manuscripts. The research work carried out by Museum staff on animals, plants, minerals and fossils, is renowned internationally and used to resolve a diverse range of problems world-wide, assisting doctors, farmers, conservationists and industry.

Growing and changing

The Natural History Museum was, administratively, a part of the British Museum until 1963 when it became an independent institution. A further development came when the Museum merged with the Geological Museum, its neighbour in Exhibition Road.

The two buildings now offer visitors the opportunity to explore earth and life sciences under one roof.

A natural history display at the old British Museum in 1845

Sir Joseph Banks, naturalist on Cook's first voyage around the world

Origins of the collections

On his death in 1753, the wealthy physician Sir Hans Sloane bequeathed his immense private collection of books, animal and plant specimens, rocks and minerals to the nation, forming the basis of the British Museum's collection. Joseph Banks, the wealthy naturalist who accompanied Captain Cook on his first voyage around the world in 1768, later bequeathed his huge herbarium to the Museum. In the latter part of the century the entire contents of the museums of the Zoological Society of London and the East India Company were acquired. Growth continued as a result of material gathered on scientific expeditions, particularly Darwin's voyage on *HMS Beagle*, and overcrowding became a major problem. A decision was taken to relocate the natural history collections and in 1881, after several years of construction, their magnificent new home, purpose built by Alfred Waterhouse, opened its doors to the public. The collections continue to grow as even today the Museum adds around half a million specimens to the collections every year.

First edition housed in the Museum's Library.

The Walter Rothschild Zoological Museum

Lionel Walter, the second Baron Rothschild, built the Zoological Museum at Tring in Hertfordshire to house his own private collection, opening it to the public in 1892. It contains over 4,000 mounted mammal and bird specimens, 40,000 bird skins and over half a million insects. When Rothschild died in 1937, he bequeathed his entire collection to The Natural History Museum.

Telephone 01442 824181 for opening times and further details.

The Natural History Museum's Darwin Centre

Inspiring discovery of the natural world.

Science changes lives. It transforms the way we see the world around us. For nearly 250 years The Natural History Museum has been at the vanguard of scientific discovery and communication, pushing boundaries and instigating ideas that have shaped our understanding of the world.

Now The Natural History Museum's Darwin Centre, currently under construction, will propel our understanding of the natural world even further by providing the facilities to allow our scientists to unlock the secrets of the 70 million specimens, many of which lie undiscovered, within its walls.

It will also provide a reference point, accessible from anywhere in the world, enabling millions to benefit from our scientists' knowledge and understanding of the natural world.

Scientific research at The Natural History Museum

An artist's impression of the Darwin Centre

An extraordinary opportunity

The Darwin Centre will be a major scientific and education complex and is the result of two decades of planning and investment. The Centre has three critical objectives:

- Revolutionising public understanding of the natural world. Enabling unprecedented access to the widest variety of animal and plant species ever assembled.
- Expanding vital scientific and research facilities. To maximise our assistance in the fight against global starvation, disease and pollution – and improve the daily lives of millions of people around the world.
- Protecting and expanding the world's foremost natural science collection as a vital scientific reference for today and a precious legacy for generations to come.

The Natural History Museum has come a long way towards achieving its goal but to take the final steps necessary in making the Darwin Centre a reality, we need your help. If you would like to know more about the Darwin Centre and how you can support it please contact The Development Office at The Natural History Museum, Cromwell Road, London SW7 5BD or call 020 7942 5266 or email supporter@nhm.ac.uk to discuss opportunities for tax effective giving at all levels.

Museum services

Museum shops

The gift shops have a wide range of souvenirs and gifts, inspired by nature, for enquiring minds of all ages, from ever-popular dinosaur models, T-shirts and games to beautiful mineral samples, microscopes, jewellery and Natural History Museum artworks. The Museum's bookshop is the foremost natural history book shop in the country, selling a full selection of the Museum's excellent publications, specialist and academic titles, popular science books and an extensive selection for children.

Refreshments

Whether you are looking for a quick snack or a main meal, we hope to be able to cater for your needs.

Life Galleries Restaurant
(Life Galleries, Gallery 35).
Family style restaurant serving hot and cold meals (from 11.30 - 14.30) along with snacks all day. Licensed.

Globe Fast Food Café
(Earth Galleries, Gallery 60).

Waterhouse Café
(Life Galleries, Gallery 11)
Speciality coffees,
sandwiches
and cakes. Licensed.

Snack Bar (Life Galleries, Basement) Chocolate, sandwiches, beverages.

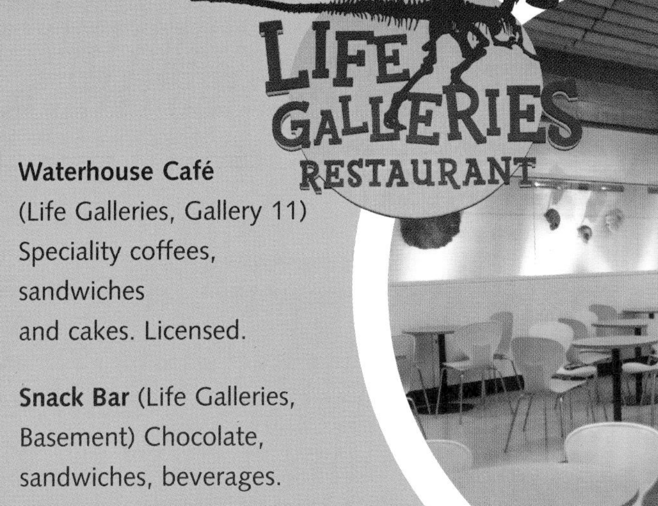

Library services

The Museum's library is a national reference library for the life and earth sciences. Its collections are of international importance with extensive holdings of early works, periodicals, current literature, artworks, maps and manuscripts. For further information on services, access details and opening hours, see *The Guide to Library and Information Services* or telephone 020 7942 5207.
Web site: http://www.nhm.ac.uk/library

Functions

The Natural History Museum is a spectacular and prestigious venue for social and business entertaining of all kinds. For information about facilities and charges please contact the Functions Manager 020 7942 5434.
Web site: http://www.nhm.ac.uk/functions

Education services

Making more of your visit

Activity sheets for children are available from the information desk and shops and help provide a focus for a family visit.
A programme of workshops, special events and gallery characters and, on occasion, opportunities to meet Museum scientists, offer visitors a chance to find out more about natural history and the Museum's scientific work. For further details visit our web site at http://www.nhm.ac.uk/education or telephone 020 7942 5555.

Beyond a visit

Adult education courses are available, offering a variety of field study tours in the UK and overseas. For further information telephone 020 7942 5001. Our Teachers' Centre offers teachers the resources to plan school, Museum and field – based classes. Teaching packs and courses are available.
Telephone 020 7942 5045 for details.

Wildlife Garden

Landscaped and planted with native British flowering plants in 1995, the Museum's Wildlife Garden demonstrates the potential for wildlife conservation and habitat creation in the inner city, it has developed into a haven for wildlife, from dragonflies to foxes.
Over 50 different species bird species alone have been recorded – robins and blackbirds frequent the garden alongside surprise visitors, pheasant and woodcock. An ongoing ecological study by Museum scientists and volunteers records the thousands of plants and animals that inhabit the garden.
The Wildlife Garden is open from April to September. Further details and information about guided tours of the garden are available from the Life Galleries information desk (Gallery 10).

Join us !

as a member...

As a visitor, it is only with membership that you can get a closer look at the Museum and its work. In addition, by being a member you will also be supporting the natural world.

Enjoy these privileges

Free entry
Free admission to The Natural History Museum as well as The Walter Rothschild Zoological Museum Collection at Tring, Hertfordshire*.

Magazine
Receive *Nature First* – a quarterly, full colour magazine offering insight into the Museum's discoveries in the natural world as well as updating you on events and exhibitions. For child and family members, we also offer the special supplement, *Tyrannosaurus times*.

Events
A fascinating range of events from behind-the-scenes tours to exhibition previews, and children's workshops.

Members' private view, BG Wildlife photographer of the Year 1999

A place of your own
The members' room offers a chance to relax and enjoy free refreshments during your visit to the Museum.

10% discount
Enjoy money off items in the Museum's shops and restaurants.
(excluding Basement Snack Bar)

* children and senior citizens now gain free entry to the Museum

Dinosaur Dig

Join now

Join today, give support to benefit the natural world and **enjoy the privileges** of membership. To become a member, ask a member of staff or complete a "Join Today" form. For any queries, or to join by credit card, call the membership office on 020 7942 5792, or email members@nhm.ac.uk